Australian Poems
to read to the
very young

This book
belongs to

Violet Jones 2014.
Love
John & Val Berriman.

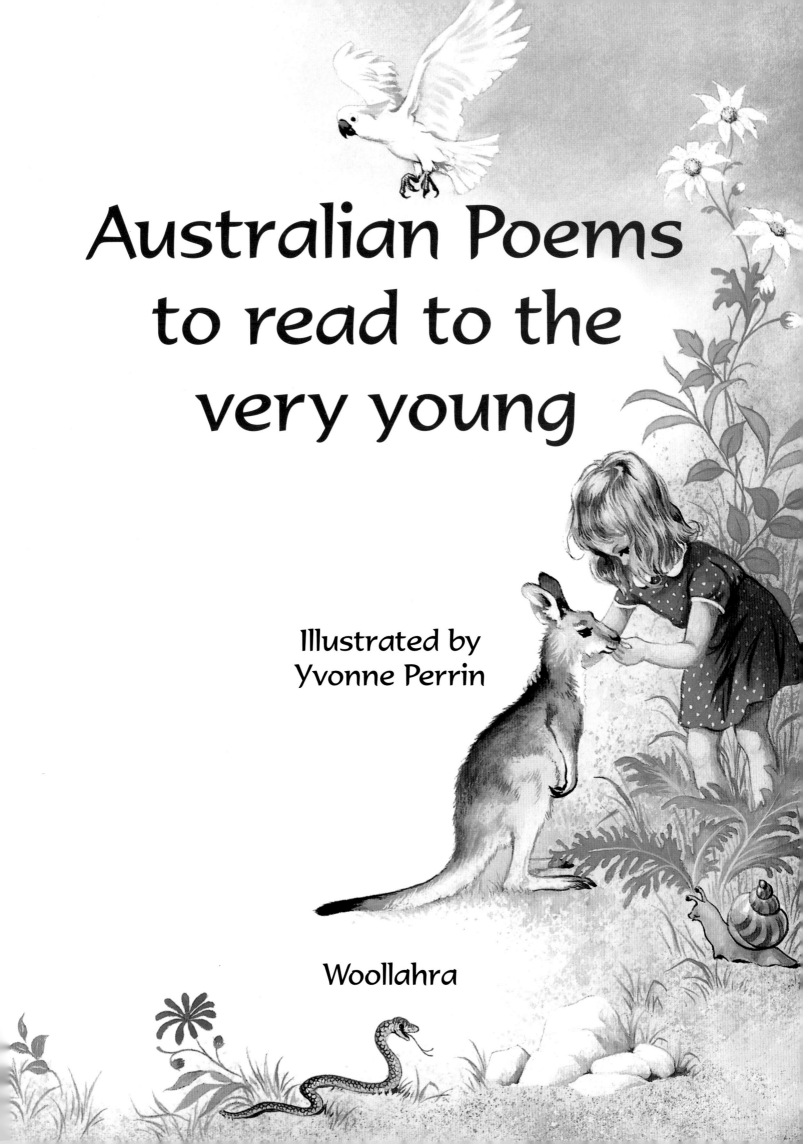

Australian Poems to read to the very young

Illustrated by
Yvonne Perrin

Woollahra

GUNDAGAI 5

CONTENTS

RUB-A-DUB-DUB

Rub-a-dub-dub,
There were THREE in the scrub,
Eating a pineapple pie,
Red Kangaroo, Mouse and Wallaby too,
When Peter Possum walked by.

Rub-a-dub-dub,
There were FOUR in the scrub,
Eating their way though the crust;
When out of the blue came Fred Cockatoo
With some cordial to wash down the dust.

Rub-a-dub-dub,
There were FIVE in the scrub,
Nothing was left but the crumbs;
But when George the Galah drove up in his car,
They were all fast asleep neath the gums.

Dan Vallely

9

A SKINKY PROBLEM

I think I'm a little skink.
I think, I think, I must.
For I have a skinky body
And I skink around the dust.
I have a skinky little tongue,
That flickers in the air,
Catching Skinkelicious insects
Of which I have my share.
It's rather a skinky problem,
So I'll have a little think.
Yes, I'm almost sure,
I've got to be.
I am a little skink!

Dan Vallely

GROWING UP

Little Tommy Tadpole began to weep and wail,
For little Tommy Tadpole had lost his little tail,
And his mother didn't know him as he wept
       upon a log;
For he wasn't Tommy Tadpole, but Mr Thomas Frog.

C.J. Dennis

BIRD SONG

I suspect the Kookaburra
For his methods are not thorough
In his highly-praised campaign against the snakes.
And the small birds, one and all,
Curse him for a cannibal~
Though he certainly is cheerful when he wakes.

C.J. Dennis

THE BEETLE

"Hum...Drum! Hum...Drum!
Beetle where are you?"
"I caught a little cold,
As I walked in the dew!
So I flew in a doorway,
And found a little toe,
Peeping through a window
In a little shoe!"

Mary Gilmore

BULLOCKY BILL

As I came down Talbingo Hill
I heard a maiden cry,
"There goes old Bill the Bullocky~
He's bound for Gundigai."

A better poor old beggar
Never cracked an honest crust,
A tougher poor old beggar
Never drug a whip through dust.

His team got bogged on Five-mile Creek,
Bill lashed and swore and cried,
"If Nobbie don't get me out of this
I'll tattoo his jolly hide."

But Nobbie strained and broke the yoke
And poked out the leader's eye,
Then the dog sat on the tucker-box
Five miles from Gundagai.

12

THE SPRINGTIME IT BRINGS ON THE SHEARING

The springtime it brings on the shearing,
And then you will see them in droves,
To the west-country stations all steering,
A seeking a job of the coves.

With a ragged old swag on my shoulder
And a billy quart-pot in my hand,
And I'll tell you we'll 'stonish the new-chum
To see how we travel the land.

Oh and after the shearing is over
And the wool season's all at an end,
It is then you will see the flash shearers
Making Johnny-cakes round in the bend.

WOOLLOOMOOLOO

Here's a ridiculous riddle for you:
How many O's are in Woolloomooloo?
Two for the W, Two for the M.
Four for the L's, and that's plenty for them.

C.J.Dennis

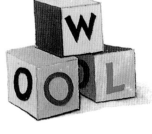

HIST!

Hist! ...... Hark!
The night is very dark,
And we've to go a mile or so
Across the Possum Park.
Step .... light,
Keeping to the right;
If we delay and lose our way,
We'll be out half the night.
The clouds are low and gloomy. Oh!
It's just begun to mist!
We haven't any overcoats
And ~ Hist! ...... Hist!

(Mo ...... poke!)
Who was that that spoke?
This is not a fitting spot
To make a silly joke.
Dear ...... me!
A mopoke in a tree!
It jarred me so, I didn't know
Whatever it could be.
But come along; creep along;
Soon we shall be missed.
They'll get a scare and wonder where
We ~ Hush! ...... Hist!

Ssh! ...... Soft!
I've told you oft and oft
We should not stray so far away
Without a moon aloft.
Oo! .... Scat!
Goodness! What was that?
Upon my word it's quite absurd,
It's only just a cat.
But come along; haste along;
Soon we'll have to rush,
Or we'll be late and find the gate
Is ~ Hist! ...... Hush!

(Kok! .... Korrock!)
Oh! I've had a shock!
I hope and trust it's only just
A frog behind a rock.
Shoo! ...... Shoo!
We've had enough of you;
Scaring folk just for a joke
Is not the thing to do.
But come along, slip along ~
Isn't it a lark
Just to roam so far from home
On ~ Hist! ...... Hark!

Look! ...... See!
Shining through the tree,
The window-light is glowing bright
To welcome you and me.
Shout! ...... Shout!
There's someone round about,
And through the door I see some more
And supper all laid out.

Now, Run! Run! Run!
Oh, we've had such splendid fun ~
Through the park in the dark,
As brave as anyone.
Laughed, we did, and chaffed we did,
And whistled all the way,
And we're home again! Home again!
Hip ...... Hooray!

C.J. Dennis

THE

Hey, there! Hoop-la! The circus is in town!
Have you seen the elephant?
Have you seen the Clown?
Have you seen the dappled horse
gallop round the ring?
Have you seen the acrobats
on the dizzy swing?
Have you seen the tumbling men
tumble up and down?
Hoop-la! Hoop-la! The circus is in town!

CIRCUS

Hey, there! Hoop-la! Here's the circus troupe!
Here's the educated dog jumping through the hoop.
See the lady Blondin with the parasol and fan,
The lad upon the ladder and the
  India-rubber man.
See the joyful juggler and the boy who
  loops the loop.
Hey! Hey! Hey! Hey! Here's the circus troupe!

C.J. Dennis

THE ANT EXPLORER

Once a little sugar ant made up his mind to roam~
To fare away far away, far away from home.
He had eaten all his breakfast, and he had his Ma's consent
To see what he should chance to see and here's the way he went~
Up and down a fern frond, round and round the stone,
Down a gloomy gully where he loathed to be alone,
Up a mighty mountain range, seven inches high,
Through the fearful forest grass that nearly hid the sky,
Out along a bracken bridge, bending in the moss,
Till he reached a dreadful desert that was feet and feet across.
Twas a dry, deserted desert, and a trackless land to tread;
He wished that he was home again and tucked-up tight
    in bed.
His little legs were wobbly, his strength was nearly spent,
And so he turned around again and here's the way he went~
Back away from desert lands feet and feet across,
Back along the bracken bridge bending in the moss,
Through the fearful forest grass, shutting out the sky,
Up a mighty mountain range seven inches high,
Down a gloomy gully, where he loathed to be alone,
Up and down a fern frond and round and round a stone.
A dreary ant, a weary ant, resolved no more to roam,
He staggered up the garden path and popped back home.

               C.J. Dennis

SAID THE CAT TO THE KITTEN

Said the cat to the kitten,
"Will you find my little mitten,
That I wore when visiting the Queen?"
Said the kitten to the cat,
"It is underneath the mat,
In the place where it always has been!"

Said the old cat, then,
"Before I count ten,
Can you find the hat I wore
When visiting the Queen?"
Said the little kitten-cat,
"You cannot have the hat,
For it's many, many years
Since the old thing was seen!"

Then the old pussy-cat
Sat down upon the mat,
And cried for the hat
She wore to see the Queen,
While the naughty little kitten
Stole the last lone mitten,
And played it was a mouse
She found upon the green.

Mary Gilmore

WALTZING MATILDA

Once a jolly swagman camped by a billabong,
Under the shade of a coolibah tree,
And he sang as he watched and waited till his billy boiled,
"Who'll come a-waltzing Matilda with me?
Waltzing Matilda, Waltzing Matilda,
Who'll come a waltzing Matilda with me?"
And he sang as he watched and waited till his billy boiled,
"Who'll come a-waltzing Matilda with me?"

Down came a jumbuck to drink at the billabong:
Up jumped the swagman and grabbed him with glee,
And he sang as he shoved that jumbuck in his tucker bag,
"You'll come a-waltzing Matilda with me
    Waltzing Matilda, Waltzing Matilda,
    You'll come a-waltzing Matilda with me."
And he sang as he shoved that jumbuck in his tucker bag,
    "You'll come a-waltzing Matilda with me."

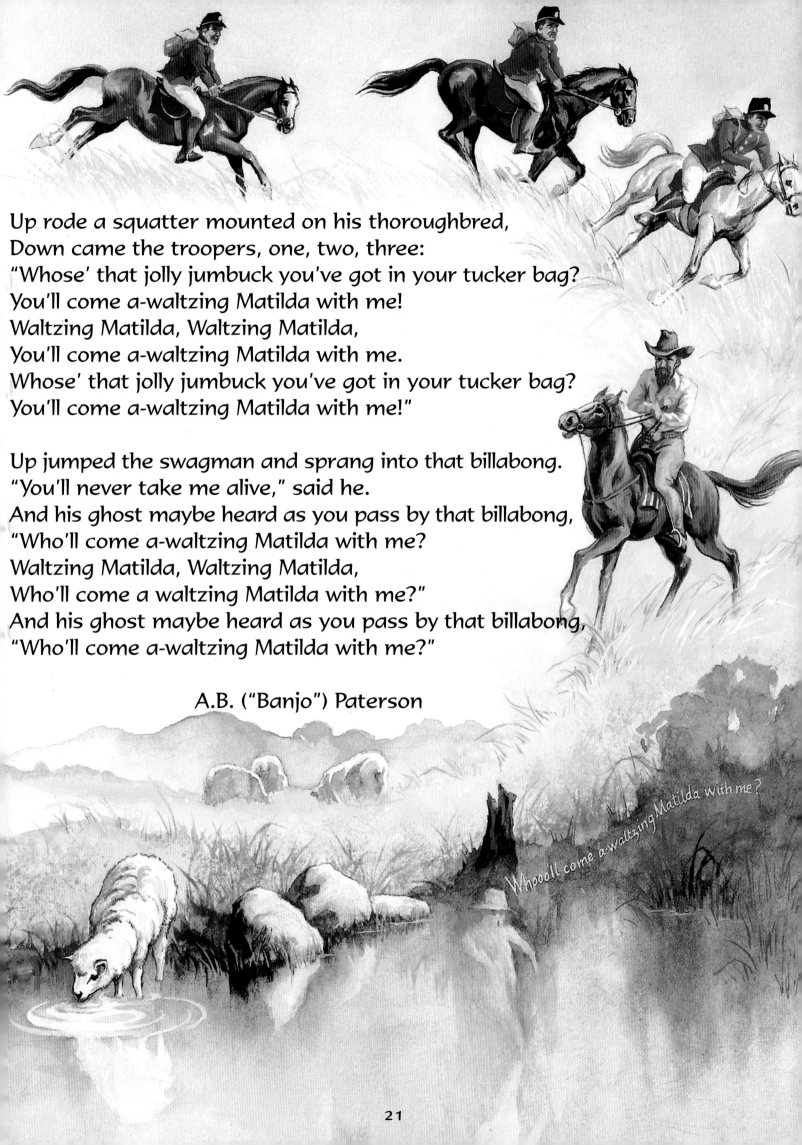

Up rode a squatter mounted on his thoroughbred,
Down came the troopers, one, two, three:
"Whose' that jolly jumbuck you've got in your tucker bag?
You'll come a-waltzing Matilda with me!
Waltzing Matilda, Waltzing Matilda,
You'll come a-waltzing Matilda with me.
Whose' that jolly jumbuck you've got in your tucker bag?
You'll come a-waltzing Matilda with me!"

Up jumped the swagman and sprang into that billabong.
"You'll never take me alive," said he.
And his ghost maybe heard as you pass by that billabong,
"Who'll come a-waltzing Matilda with me?
Waltzing Matilda, Waltzing Matilda,
Who'll come a waltzing Matilda with me?"
And his ghost maybe heard as you pass by that billabong,
"Who'll come a-waltzing Matilda with me?"

A.B. ("Banjo") Paterson

Whooo'll come a-waltzing Matilda with me?

OUR STREET

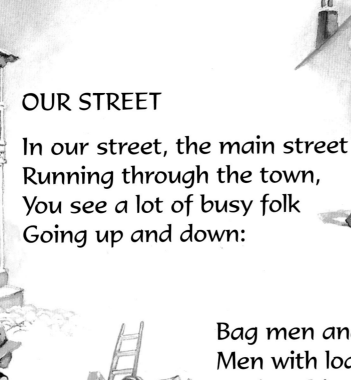

In our street, the main street
Running through the town,
You see a lot of busy folk
Going up and down:

Bag men and basket men,
Men with loads of hay,
Buying things and selling things
And carting things away.

The butcher is a funny man,
He calls me Dandy Dick;
The baker is a cross man,
I think he's often sick;

The fruiterer's a nice man,
He gives me apples, too;
The grocer says, "Good morning boy,
What can I do for you?"

Of all the men in our street
I like the cobber best,
Tapping, tapping at his last
Without a minutes rest;

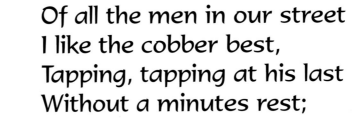

Talking all the time he taps,
Driving in the nails
Smiling with his old grey eyes ~
(Hush) ... telling fairy tales.

C.J. Dennis

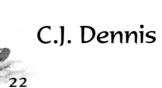

TEA TALK

"Excuse me if I sit on you," the cup said to the saucer.
"I fear I've been here all the afternoon."
"Spare excuses," said the saucer; "you have sat on me before, sir."
"Oh, I'll stir him up directly," said the spoon.
"Stop your clatter!" Stop the clatter!" cried the bread and butter platter.
"Tittle-tattle!" sneered the teapot, with a shrug;
"Now the most important question is my chronic indigestion."
"Ah, you've taken too much tannin," jeered the jug.
"Hey, hey, hey!" sang the silver-plated tray,
"It's time you had your faces washed. I've come to clear away!"

C.J. Dennis

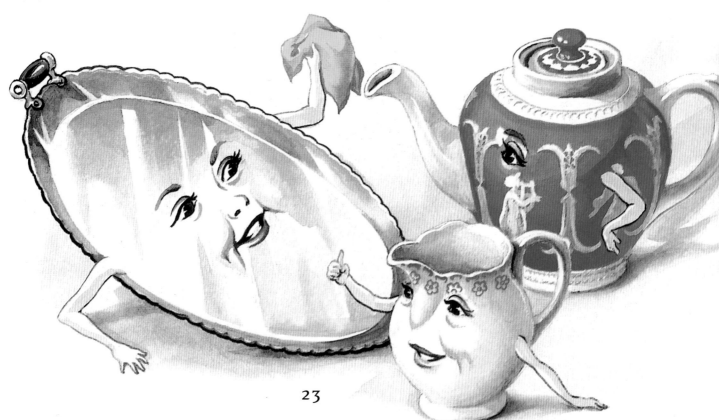

THE SWAGMAN

Oh, he was old and he was spare;
His bushy whiskers and hair
Were all fussed up and very grey
He said he'd come a long, long way
And had a long, long way to go.
Each boot was broken at the toe.
And he'd a swag upon his back.
His billy-can, as black as black,
Was just the thing for making tea
At picnics, so it seemed to me.

'Twas hard to earn a bite of bread,
He told me. Then he shook his head,
And all the little corks that hung
Around his hat-brim danced & swung
And bobbed about his face; and when
I laughed he made them dance again.
He said they were for keeping flies ~
"The pesky varmints" ~ from his eyes.
He called me "Codger" ... "Now you see
The best days of your life," Said he.
"But days will come to bend your back,
And, when they come, keep off the track.
Keep off, young codger, if you can."
He seemed a funny sort of man.

He told me that he wanted work,
But jobs were scarce this side of Bourke,
And he supposed he'd have to go
Another fifty miles or so.
"Nigh all my life the track I've walked,"
He said. I liked the way he talked.
And oh, the places he had seen!
I don't know where he had not been ~
On every road, in every town,
All through the country, up and down.
"Young codger, shun the track," he said.
And put his hand upon my head.
I noticed, then, that his old eyes
Were very blue and very wise.
"Ay, once I was a little lad,"
He said, and seemed to grow quite sad.

I sometimes think: When I'm a man,
I'll get a good black billy-can
And hang some corks around my hat
And lead a jolly life like that.

C.J. Dennis

THE TRIANTIWONTIGONGOLOPE

There's a very funny insect that you do not often spy,
And it isn't quite a spider, and it isn't quite a fly;
It is something like a beetle, and a little like a bee,
But nothing like a woolly grub that
climbs upon a tree.
Its name is quite a hard one, but you'll
learn it soon, I hope.
So, try …
Tri ~
Tri~anti~wonti ~
Triantiwontigongolope.

It lives on weeds and wattle-gum, and has a funny face;
Its appetite is hearty, and its manners a disgrace.
When first you come upon it, it will
give you quite a scare,
But when you look for it again you find it isn't there.
And unless you call it softly it will stay
away and mope.
So, try …
Tri ~
Tri~anti~wonti ~
Triantiwontigongolope.

26

It trembles if you tickle it or tread upon its toes;
It is not an early riser, but it has a snubbish nose.
If you sneer at it, or scold it, it will scuttle off in shame,
But it purrs and purrs quite proudly if you
call it by its name,
And offer it some sandwiches of sealing-wax and soap.
So, try ...
Tri ~
Tri~anti~wonti ~
Triantiwontigongolope.

But of course you haven't seen it; and I truthfully confess
That I haven't seen it either, and I don't know its address.
For there isn't such an insect, though there
really might have been
If the trees and grass were purple, and the sky
was bottle-green.
It's just a little joke of mine,
which you'll forgive, I hope.
Oh, try ...
Tri ~
Tri~anti~wonti ~
Triantiwontigongolope.

C.J. Dennis

THE KOOKABURRA

When the little brown knees of the spider
are folded in sleep,
And she hangs on her web in a tiny round heap,
Kookaburra will wake,
And his head he will shake,
And laughing will sing,
"Kook-kook-kook-burra, burra-burra.
Kookaburra-burra! Kookaburra-burra!"
And down from his branch will float on his wing.
Then the wee spotted snake in the grass will be shaken
with fright,
And he'll hope that a tussock may hide him from sight,
But the bird in the air,
Will exclaim, "I declare!"
And chuckling will sing,
"Kook-kook-kook-burra, burra-burra!
Kookaburra-burra! Kookaburra-burra!"
And up to his tree the snake he will bring.
"But why did you do it?"
A little boy said.
"Because," laughed the bird,
"I had to be fed!"

Mary Gilmore

THE NEW ENGLAND COCKY

'Twas a New England cocky, as of late I've been told,
Who died, so 'tis said, on account of the cold.
When dying he called to his children, "Come here!
As I'm dying I want my fortune to share.

"Dear children, you know I've toiled early and late,
I've struggled with Nature and wrestled with Fate.
Then all do your best to my fortune repair;
And to my son John I leave a dear native bear.

"To Mary I give my pet kangaroo,
May it prove to turn out a great blessing, too;
To Michael I leave the old cockatoo,
And to Bridget I'll give the piebald emu.

"To the others whatever is left I will leave ~
Don't quarrel, or else my poor spirit will grieve;
There's fish in the stream and fowl on the lake,
Let each have as much as any may take.

"And now, my dear children, no more can I do,
My fortune I've fairly divided with you."
And these were the last words his children did hear ~
"Don't forget that I reared you on pumpkin and bear."

29

The End

Other titles in this series:

Possum One the Outback Rocketship
Professor Cockatoo's Amazing Weatherdust
Possum Creek's Big Flood
The Great Possum Creek Bush Fire
The Great Possum Creek Earthquake
The Lost World of Possum Creek
The Great Possum Creek Drought
The Possum Creek Olympics

Also illustrated by Yvonne Perrin:

Banjo Paterson's Animals Noah Forgot

ISBN 1-876553-14-6

9 781876 553142